Harry the Hedgehog woke up, uncurled himself out of a ball and stretched. He shook the remaining leaves from his spikes and poked his little black nose outside his house of leaves and twigs in the compost heap.

He was very hungry!

He began ambling around the garden and found a gooey snail which he gobbled up. He continued his rambling and found a fat caterpillar which he crunched and munched. He found a tasty, yummy, slimy slug…

SLURP!

Harry was full.
However, Harry had spent a long, cold winter asleep
and he was lonely…

He wanted a friend to talk to.

Harry squinted.

He looked across the garden and recognised Billy the Badger standing near the garden pond.

Billy might be Harry's friend.

Billy the Badger is known to be rough and gruff.
But Harry tried anyway.

"Hello Billy, I am Harry the Hedgehog...
will you be my friend?" he asked gently.

"No, Harry, you are too small and I might squash you,"
replied Billy in a grumpy voice.
"You cannot be my friend."

It might not be such a good idea to have Billy the Badger as a friend.
He is a bit too burly and surly.
But Harry had spent a long, cold winter asleep and he was lonely.
He wanted a friend to talk to.

Harry walked under the oak tree and spotted Sammy the Grey Squirrel, scampering along the garden fence in search of nuts.

Sammy might be Harry's friend.
Sammy the Grey Squirrel is a bit bossy, though.

But Harry tried anyway.

"Hello Sammy, I am Harry the Hedgehog...
will you be my friend?" he asked timidly.

"No Harry, you are too slow and you are not able to climb trees.
You would never be able to keep up with me," replied Sammy in a sharp,
snappy voice. "You cannot be my friend."

It might not be such a good idea to have Sammy the Squirrel as a friend.
He is a bit too bossy. Poor Harry! He had spent a long, cold winter
asleep, and he was so lonely.

Harry spied the old wooden shed where Freddy the Fox was smelling, sniffing and searching the ground.

Freddy might be Harry's friend.
Freddy the Fox is known to be cunning and clever.

But Harry tried anyway.

"Hello Freddy, I am Harry the Hedgehog.
Will you be my friend?" asked Harry cautiously.
"Oh yes Harry, I am just about to have dinner, you can be my friend!"
Freddy the Fox replied, with a sly smile.

Freddy snarled and pounced at Harry.

Run Harry, run! Harry ran and ran and ran – around the garden as fast
as his little legs would carry him. Away from Freddy the Fox, who was
very crafty, past Sammy the Grey Squirrel who was searching for nuts
near the big oak tree, and past the garden pond where Billy the Badger
was sniffing at a watering can.

Harry was out of breath. He rested beside a big log heap near the hawthorn hedge.

Poor Harry! He had spent a long, cold winter asleep and he was still very lonely. Where could he find a friend, who was not too rough, too bossy or too crafty?

He stared longingly through the nettle patch and saw Holly. Holly was a beautiful hedgehog.

Harry was shy. But he tried anyway.

"Hello Holly, I am Harry the Hedgehog.
Will you be my friend?" asked Harry hesitantly.

Holly might be Harry's friend.
Holly the Hedgehog smiled. "Of course I would love be your friend,"
Holly replied in a kind, quiet voice.

Harry had spent a long, cold winter asleep and he was not lonely any
more. Now Harry and Holly love to ramble around the garden, past the
pond, under the oak tree, and near the garden shed where they keep a
close eye for Freddy the Fox! They are happy gobbling up gooey snails,
crunching fat caterpillars and slurping yummy, slimy slugs.

CARING FOR HEDGEHOGS IN YOUR GARDEN

MAKE YOUR OWN 'HEDGEHOG HOTEL'

We can all help Hedgehogs by doing a little less gardening and providing a wild corner for them to search for food and possibly use as a home in the winter. Hedgehogs are a gardener's best friend and munch up slugs, snails, beetles and other invertebrates.

Letting a corner of the garden be a bit messier with long grass, maybe a wildflower meadow and leaves is a great way of providing a habitat for hedgehogs. Building a log pile or having a pile of leaves collected in a compost heap is also a great help and a place to locate a 'hedgehog hotel'.

If you are handy with tools and timber, you could construct a hedgehog home similar to the one shown in the photographs. However, you can make simple ones that will last a winter using sturdy cardboard boxes or milk crates. Protect them with a plastic covering and then surround with leaves and soil. Make sure to leave air vents and an opening of at least 12 cm square.

Make your own hedgehog hotel

BE CAREFUL USING SHARP TOOLS! GET A GROWN-UP TO GIVE YOU A HAND.

TIPS:
- Timber boxes are ideal, if you have the material and tools to make them. Just be careful using sharp tools. But you can make hedgehog hotels in many ways. Just try and have an opening of at least 12 cm, and then either make a second door inside your box, or build a separate 'corridor' entrance.

CONSIDER...
- Place your hotel in a quiet corner of the garden. Disguise it with leaves, but make sure the entrance is not covered. Keep it on or above ground level. Cover the roof with roofing felt. Make the roof at a slight angle to help keep the rain away from the inside.

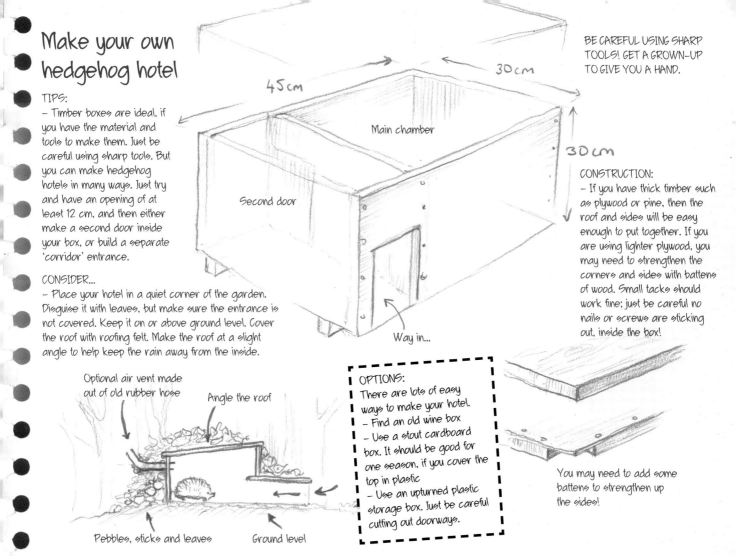

45cm

30cm

Main chamber

Second door

30cm

Way in...

CONSTRUCTION:
- If you have thick timber such as plywood or pine, then the roof and sides will be easy enough to put together. If you are using lighter plywood, you may need to strengthen the corners and sides with battens of wood. Small tacks should work fine; just be careful no nails or screws are sticking out, inside the box!

Optional air vent made out of old rubber hose

Angle the roof

OPTIONS:
There are lots of easy ways to make your hotel.
- Find an old wine box
- Use a stout cardboard box. It should be good for one season, if you cover the top in plastic
- Use an upturned plastic storage box. Just be careful cutting out doorways.

You may need to add some battens to strengthen up the sides!

Pebbles, sticks and leaves

Ground level

HEDGEHOG DO'S AND DON'TS

DO: help by leaving out food. Meat-based dog and cat food, unsalted crushed peanuts, sunflower hearts, dried meal worms, and dried fruit. There are even specialist hedgehog foods available. Fresh water in a shallow dish is also very important too.

DO: less gardening. Provide long grass, grow a wildflower meadow, create log piles, make heaps of dry leaves.

DO: put bricks or ladders in garden ponds so hedgehogs can escape if they fall in.

DON'T: leave out cow's milk and bread. Hedgehogs will eat it but it makes them very sick. They then get diarrhoea which is yucky!

DON'T: use pesticides, rodenticides or slug pellets as all are harmful to hedgehogs who are affected through the food chain. Try alternatives such as beer traps, seaweed, crushed egg shells, coffee grounds, copper protection and garlic around delicate plants that need protection from hungry slugs.

DON'T: leave litter around; hedgehogs (and other wildlife) often get caught in plastic, bottles and cans!

NATURE DETECTIVE (Tracks and signs)

Throughout **Harry the Hedgehog**, you may have seen some prints and trails. Many of the animals visiting our gardens do so at night when we are asleep and not watching, so to see evidence of their visits, we have to look for tracks and signs. Some signs to look out for are scats (poo) or evidence of them scratching the ground for food.

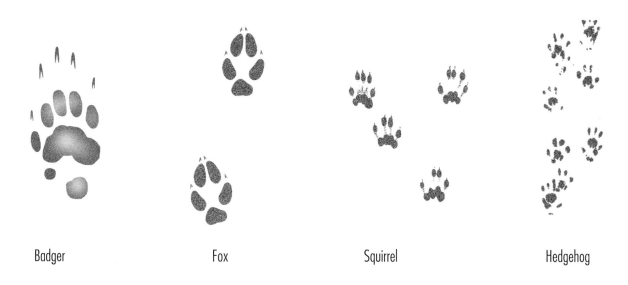

| Badger | Fox | Squirrel | Hedgehog |

I'd like to thank Jennifer, my ever patient partner in life for her encouragement and abilities with the big red pen, Declan Kenny from the Drawing Board for his amazing photography and design skills and shared passion for wildlife and mischief! Mr Paddy Smith, Mr Tomas Donegan, and Ms Catherine Creedon for their editorial experience and for keeping me realistic!

Most of all I would like to thank all the boys and girls, mums and dads, nanas and grandads, teachers and carers who have come out over the years to see our Naturally Wild presentations and listen to my stories, musings and really bad jokes!